My First...
School Day

Eve Marleau and Michael Garton

QED Publishing

On Monday, Dad takes Kai to **primary school**. It's Kai's first day and he's a bit worried.

"Dad, I don't want to go to school. I won't know anyone and I will miss Barney."

My First...
School Day

First published in the UK in 2009 by
QED Publishing
A Quarto Group Company
226 City Road
London EC1V 2TT
www.qed-publishing.co.uk

A catalogue record for this book is available
from the British Library.

ISBN 978 1 84835 261 2

Author Eve Marleau
Illustrator Michael Garton
Consultants Shirley Bickler and Tracey Dils
Designer Elaine Wilkinson

Publisher Steve Evans
Creative Director Zeta Davies
Managing Editor Amanda Askew

Printed and bound in China

The words in **bold** are
explained in the glossary
on page 24.

"I'm sure you'll make some new friends. All the other boys and girls will be feeling exactly the same as you," says Dad.

"Hello! Welcome to
Reception Class.
My name is Miss James."

"Hello," says Dad. "This is Kai."

"Hello, Kai. Would you like
to sit with Lucas and Max?"
Kai nods.

"Good morning, Reception Class. Please sit on the carpet so I can take the **register**."

"When I call out your name, say 'Yes, Miss James' and tell us all something about yourself."

"Ama?"

Yes, Miss James. My dad is a firefighter.

“Ben?”

“Kai?”

Yes, Miss James. I have two big brothers.
Yes, Miss James. My dog is called Barney.

"First, I'm going to put you in special **groups**. You will work in these groups every day.

"Ben, Lisa, Jane, Steven and Alison are the yellow rockets."

"Ama, Clare, Lucas, Toby and Susie are the green rockets."

10

"Max, Julia, Caroline, Tamzin and Nieve are the blue rockets."

"Kai, Sarah, Daniel, Matthew and Fran are the red rockets."

"This morning, you're going to draw your favourite thing. Then I'll put all your drawings on the wall."

Kai draws Barney, Sarah draws a pony and Fran draws a teddy bear.

Max draws
a red car.

Lucas draws an **astronaut**.

13

Ring! Ring! It's break time.

The children each take an apple
from Miss James and go outside.

Julia, Caroline and Nieve sit on
the bench eating their apples.

Kai plays catch with Max and Matthew.

Clare, Lucas and Toby play tag.

After break time, Miss James reads them a story about a rabbit called Josh and his adventure on a train.

"Woooo Wooooo!"

Miss James reads.

"Pull the train's whistle, children."

16

"Woooo WOOOOO!"

says the whole class as they move around the room. Kai says it as loudly as he can.

After story time, Miss James asks the children about their favourite animals.

I like dogs because I have a dog called Barney.

I like lions because they roar!

18

I like mice because they're sweet.

I like monkeys because they swing through trees.

19

Ring! Ring!

The bell rings
at 12 o'clock.

"Normally it would be time for lunch. Today, as it's your very first day, you can go home now."

"Yay!"

Outside the school,
Mum and Barney wait
for Kai. "Did you have
a nice morning?"

"Yes, I did!

I drew a picture
of Barney."

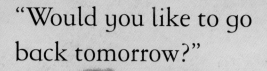

"Would you like to go back tomorrow?"

"Yes please!"

23

Glossary

Astronaut A person who travels into space in a rocket or spacecraft.

Break time A short time between lessons.

Group Several people who have been put together.

Primary school A school for children aged between four and 11.

Reception Class The youngest class in primary school.

Register A list of the children's names in a class.